INSPIRE
HAIR FASHION FOR SALON CLIENTS

Table of

Featuring: Vidal Sassoon - Salon A·K·S -Toni & Guy

Jacques Dessange - Robert of Philadelphia

Volume
38

30+

Contents

BEFORE

SHORT

FRANCESCO GROUP
PHOTO: PETER DELLICOMPAGNI

FRANCESCO GROUP
PHOTO: PETER DELLICOMPAGNI

SHAMPOO
HAIR: LISA MACKAY NAYLOR
MAKE-UP: REBECCA FRYE
PHOTO: SIDNEY G. THOMPSON III

Smoldering
HOT! HOT! HOT!
Hair like this begs to have
fingers run through it.

Palm Springs
Sophisticate

This look oozes
elegance and **style**
without trying too hard!

Bedroom Eyes & Hair!

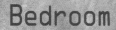

Strikingly SEXY,
this look whispers of things to come.

Blond Bombshell -
There is nothing subtle about this look!

It screams SEXY!

Blonde Momshell! Who says Moms can't be Sexy?

This playful blonde on blonde wears a casual
yet sexy style that gives her many styling options.

Hair Graphix - Sam Lavella

RED

with Envy!

Warm tones
bring added
life to a

short
sexy
style

supported
by great bone
structure.

Hair Graphix
Sam Lavella

HAIR GRAPHIX
HAIR: SAM LAVELLA
MAKE-UP: SHAWNDELLE JONES
PHOTO: SAM LAVELLA

BAZZAK HAIR DESIGN & DAY SPA
HAIR: MARZIE MOHAMMADI
MAKE-UP: MARZIE MOHAMMADI
PHOTO: TOM CARSON

MICHAEL RAYMOND SALON
HAIR: KENLEY
MAKE-UP: CAROL
PHOTO: RICK YEATTS

BAZZAK HAIR DESIGN & DAY SPA
HAIR: ERIN FENSTOMOCHER
MAKE-UP: ERIN FENSTOMOCHER
PHOTO: TOM CARSON

BAZZAK HAIR DESIGN & DAY SPA
HAIR: MARZIE MOHAMMADI
MAKE-UP: MARZIE MOHAMMADI
PHOTO: TOM CARSON

SCISSOR HANDS
HAIR: SHERI CORTELLONI
PHOTO: LAURA RADKE

COR DE KAPPER
HAIR: GRAZIA VAN HEDEL
PHOTO: FRED DE WERDT

Chestnut color was used for the feel of autumn - combined with spring s coppergold and fire-red from the burning summer sun.

Cor de Kapper - Barry Loos

For this look, we darkened the lower part of the haircut by using a dark maroon color.

Cor de Kapper - Barry Loos

MR. VINNIE HAIRSTYLING
HAIR: MISTER VINNIE
MAKE-UP: MICHELLE BOHM
PHOTO: ROBERT M. VINOVICH

GJOKO INTERNATIONAL HAIR SALON
HAIR: GJOKO
MAKE-UP: MARY AYRES
PHOTO: SUSAN WOOG WAGNER

DAVID'S BEAUTIFUL PEOPLE
HAIR: MASSIMO
MAKE-UP: NINA RAZA

KATHY ADAMS SALON
HAIR: KATHY MCCAFFREY
MAKE-UP: BILLY RISSUTO
PHOTO: FRED SMITH

This client was given a very short, funky
haircut all done with a feather razor
to better suit her spunky personality.
Afterwards, hair was foil highlighted to
a very pale, almost white blonde. The
dramatic color compliments the haircut.
Kathy Adams Salon - Kathy McCaffrey

HOLLYWOOD HAIR

9

ROBERT OF PHILADELPHIA
HAIR: LOUIS SALVATI
MAKE-UP: ANDREY
PHOTO: ERIC VON LOCKHART

BEFORE

ROBERT OF PHILADELPHIA
HAIR: JULIE LAMB
MAKE-UP: ANDREY
PHOTO: ERIC VON LOCKHART

SHORT

BEFORE

11

ROBERT OF PHILADELPHIA
HAIR: LOUIS SALVATI
MAKE-UP: ANDREY
PHOTO: ERIC VON LOCKHART

ROBERT OF PHILADELPHIA
HAIR: LOUIS SALVATI
MAKE-UP: ANDREY
PHOTO: ERIC VON LOCKHART

ROBERT OF PHILADELPHIA
HAIR: ROBERT DILELLA
COLOR: TRACY DILELLA
MAKE-UP: KIM WOOD
PHOTO: ERIC VON LOCKHART

ROBERT OF PHILADELPHIA
HAIR: JULIE LAMB
MAKE-UP: MICHELLE LOUISELLE
PHOTO: ERIC VON LOCKHART

BEFORE

15

BEFORE

ARTISTIC HAIR
HAIR: BARBARA NOLASCO
MAKE-UP: JAIME QUEENIN
PHOTO: TAGGART-WINTERHALTER

SHORT

17

Blondes are going to be much softer this season. More delicate tones with subtle contrast.

Salon De Dawn - Dawn Orlow-Townsend

BEFORE

Highlights are becoming very
fine and delicate veins of color.
Vibe Studio - Laura Croft/Barbara Hernandez

VIBE STUDIO
HAIR: LAURA CROFT & BARBARA HERNANDEZ
MAKE-UP: JULIE STODDARD
PHOTO: TAGGART-WINTERHALTER

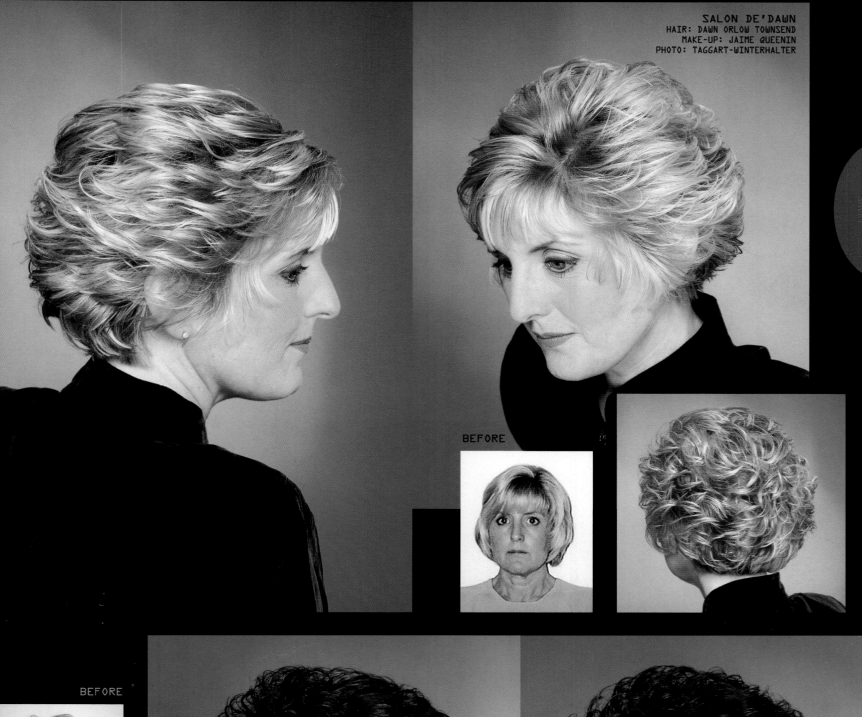

SALON DE'DAWN
HAIR: DAWN ORLOW TOWNSEND
MAKE-UP: JAIME QUEENIN
PHOTO: TAGGART-WINTERHALTER

BEFORE

BEFORE

VIBE STUDIO
HAIR: LAURA CROFT & DEBBIE WATSON
MAKE-UP: JULIE STODDARD
PHOTO: TAGGART-WINTERHALTER

Soft Wispy Bangs add the perfect finishing touch to this short and rounded style.
Vibe Studio - Laura Croft/Debbie Watson

oretta has a fun look that blends a heavier bang into longer sides with fullness around the top.

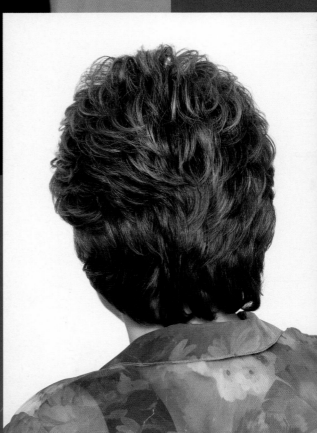

BEFORE

BEFORE

ARTISTIC HAIR
HAIR: TRACY DORAME
MAKE-UP: JULIE STODDARD
PHOTO: TAGGART-WINTERHALTER

Vibe Studio
Laura Croft/Barbara Hernandez

VIBE STUDIO
HAIR: LAURA CROFT & BARBARA HERNANDEZ
MAKE-UP: JAIME QUEENIN
PHOTO: TAGGART-WINTERHALTER

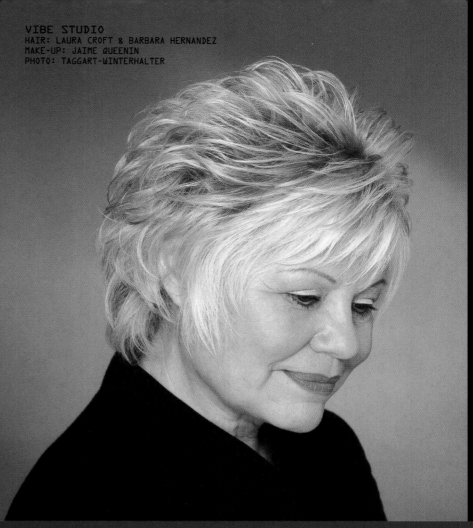

SHORT

This cute short look has height in the crown.   Artistic Hair - Tracy Dorame

BEFORE

ROBERT OF PHILADELPHIA
HAIR: MARY DODSON
MAKE-UP: MICHELLE LOUISELLE
PHOTO: ERIC VON LOCKHART

BEFORE

24

ROBERT OF PHILADELPHIA
HAIR: EDGAR AMAYA
MAKE-UP: ANDREY
PHOTO: ERIC VON LOCKHART

ROBERT OF PHILADELPHIA
HAIR: DIANA MANN
COLOR: TRACEY DILELLA
MAKE-UP: ANDREY
PHOTO: ERIC VON LOCKHART

BEFORE

ROBERT OF PHILADELPHIA
HAIR: ROBERT DILELLA
COLOR: NANCY GLORIOSO/TRACEY DILELLA
MAKE-UP: ANDREY
PHOTO: ERIC VON LOCKHART

BEFORE

ROBERT OF PHILADELPHIA
HAIR: EDGAR AMAYA
MAKE-UP: MICHELLE LOUISELLE
PHOTO: ERIC VON LOCKHART

ROBERT OF PHILADELPHIA
HAIR: NANCY GLORIOSO
COLOR: DAVID TOMLIN
MAKE-UP: MICHELLE TOMLIN
PHOTO: ERIC VON LOCKHART

ROBERT OF PHILADELPHIA
HAIR: NANCY GLORIOSO
MAKE-UP: ANDREY
PHOTO: ERIC VON LOCKHART

ROBERT OF PHILADELPHIA
HAIR: JULIE GOGGIN
MAKE-UP: MICHELLE LOUISELLE
PHOTO: ERIC VON LOCKHART

I used darker pieces
to break through this

sassy
short
style

to add texture.

Carter T. Lund & Associates
Carter T. Lund

BEFORE

CARTER T. LUND & ASSOCIATES
HAIR: CARTER T. LUND
MAKE-UP: JULIE STODDARD
PHOTO: TAGGART-WINTERHALTER

31

SALON DE DAWN
HAIR: DAWN ORLOW TOWNSEND
MAKE-UP: JULIE STODDARD
PHOTO: TAGGART-WINTERHALTER

BEFORE

32

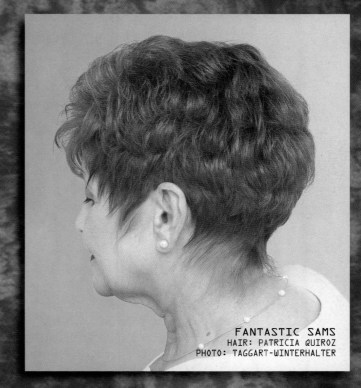

FANTASTIC SAMS
HAIR: KERRI SMITH
PHOTO: TAGGART-WINTERHALTER

FANTASTIC SAMS
HAIR: PATRICIA QUIROZ
PHOTO: TAGGART-WINTERHALTER

FANTASTIC SAMS
HAIR: TONI NEISBITT & NANCY SIMMONS
PHOTO: TAGGART-WINTERHALTER

FANTASTIC SAMS
HAIR: LAURA EDMUNDS
PHOTO: TAGGART-WINTERHALTER

VIBE STUDIO
HAIR: LAURA CROFT & BARBARA HERNANDEZ
MAKE-UP: JAIME QUEENIN
PHOTO: TAGGART-WINTERHALTER

BEFORE

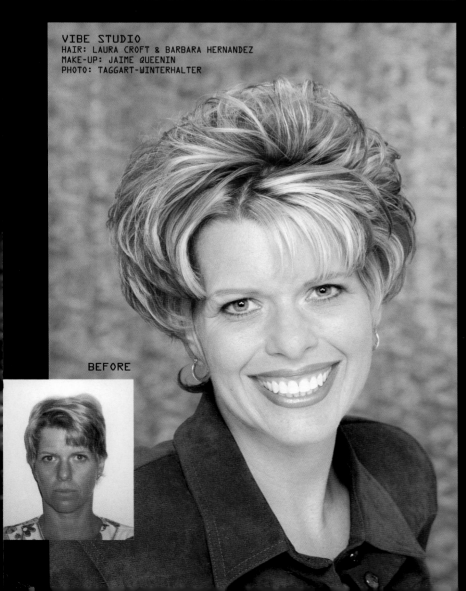

The **Classic Bob** is kicked up in the back creating a fuller look.

FANTASTIC SAMS
HAIR: JENNIFER METZGER
PHOTO: TAGGART-WINTERHALTER

CAROLYN'S
HAIR: SHANE MCDONALD
PHOTO: SHANE MCDONALD

HAUSFELD'S SALONS
HAIR: JEN BREWSTER & BRIGITTE MILES
MAKE-UP: JEN BREWSTER
PHOTO: NICK FALZERANO

Medium

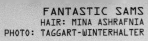

FANTASTIC SAMS
HAIR: MINA ASHRAFNIA
PHOTO: TAGGART-WINTERHALTER

Kick
it up a
Notch!

Tons of
Texture
in back for
a fun
young
look!

FANTASTIC SAMS
HAIR: BARBARA LEAL
PHOTO: TAGGART-WINTERHALTER

MEDIUM

41

ROBERT OF PHILADELPHIA
HAIR: LOUIS SALVATI
MAKE-UP: MICHELLE LOUISELLE
PHOTO: ERIC VON LOCKHART

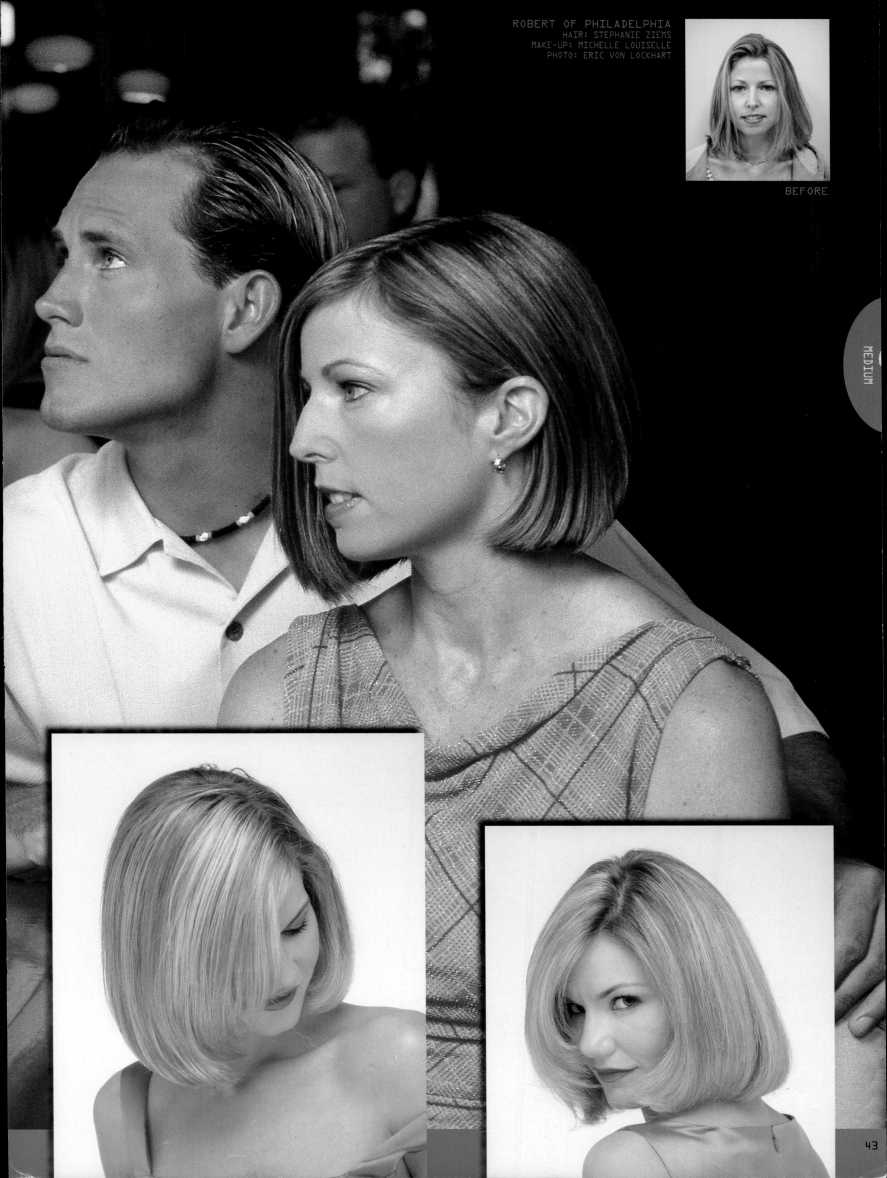

ROBERT OF PHILADELPHIA
HAIR: STEPHANIE ZIEMS
MAKE-UP: MICHELLE LOUISELLE
PHOTO: ERIC VON LOCKHART

BEFORE

MEDIUM

43

BEFORE

ROBERT OF PHILADELPHIA
HAIR: ROBERT DILELLA
MAKE-UP: ANDREY
PHOTO: ERIC VON LOCKHART

ROBERT OF PHILADELPHIA
HAIR: NANCY GLORIOSA/DAVID TOMLIN
MAKE-UP: KIM WOOD
PHOTO: ERIC VON LOCKHART

ROBERT OF PHILADELPHIA
HAIR: LISA REYNOLDS/JULIE GOGGIN
COLOR: DAVID TOMLIN
MAKE-UP: ANDREY
PHOTO: ERIC VON LOCKHART

BEFORE

ROBERT OF PHILADELPHIA
HAIR: NANCY GLORIOSA
MAKE-UP: ANDREY
PHOTO: ERIC VON LOCKHART

MEDIUM

BEFORE

47

BEFORE

BEFORE

ROBERT OF PHILADELPHIA
HAIR: KELLI HOUSEMAN
MAKE-UP: ANDREY
PHOTO: ERIC VON LOCKHART

Smooth Shorter Styles

are versatile and easy to maintain.

LONG

BAZZAK HAIR DESIGN & DAY SPA
HAIR: PARI
MAKE-UP: PARI
PHOTO: TOM CARSON

BAZZAK HAIR DESIGN & DAY SPA
HAIR: JOEY R. DOTSON
MAKE-UP: JOEY R. DOTSON
PHOTO: TOM CARSON

SHAMPOO
HAIR: LISA MACKAY NAYLOR & JOE SERLETO
MAKE-UP: REBECCA FRYE
PHOTO: SIDNEY G. THOMPSON III

GJOKO INTERNATIONAL HAIR SALON
HAIR: GJOKO
MAKE-UP: MARY AYRES
PHOTO: SUSAN WOOG WAGNER

BEFORE

Longer Layers create Volume for a soft sultry look that can be worn up or down.

BEFORE

BEFORE

ROBERT OF PHILADELPHIA
HAIR: ROBERT DILELLA
COLOR: KELLI HOUSEMAN
MAKE-UP: ANDREY
PHOTO: ERIC VON LOCKHART

ROBERT OF PHILADELPHIA
HAIR: DIANA MANN
COLOR: TRACY DILELLA
MAKE-UP: ANDREY
PHOTO: ERIC VON LOCKHART

ROBERT OF PHILADELPHIA
HAIR: JAY HATT
MAKE-UP: ANDREY
PHOTO: ERIC VON LOCKHART

BEFORE

BEFORE

ROBERT OF PHILADELPHIA
HAIR: JULIE GOGGIN
MAKE-UP: ANDREY
PHOTO: ERIC VON LOCKHART

57

ROBERT OF PHILADELPHIA
HAIR: KELLI HOUSEMAN
MAKE-UP: MICHELLE LOUISELLE
PHOTO: ERIC VON LOCKHART

58

...T OF PHILADELPHIA
HAIR: ROBERT DILELLA
COLOR: TRACEY DILELLA
...EUP: ANDREY
...HOTO: ERIC VON LOCKHART

LONG

BEFORE

ROBERT OF PHILADELPHIA
HAIR: DIANA MANN
MAKE-UP: ANDREY
PHOTO: ERIC VON LOCKHART

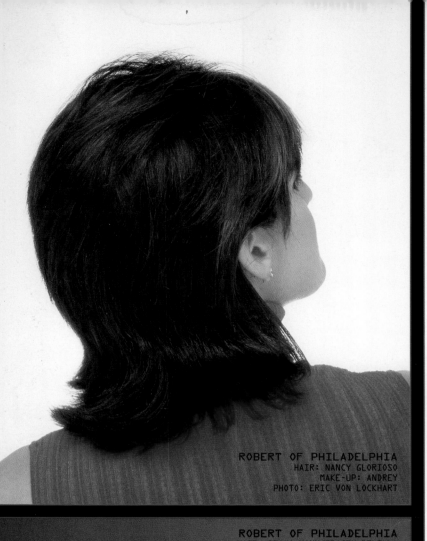

LONG

CARTER T. LUND & ASSOCIATES
HAIR: CARTER T. LUND
MAKE-UP: JAIME QUEENIN
PHOTO: TAGGART-WINTERHALTER

LONG

63

FANTASTIC SAMS
HAIR: PATTI MEAD
PHOTO: TAGGART-WINTERHALTER

AMOUR HAIR DESIGN
HAIR: LIZ KAHLER
MAKE-UP: JULIE STODDARD
PHOTO: TAGGART-WINTERHALTER

Longer Layers
create movement
and give hair

tons of **dimension**

FANTASTIC SAMS
HAIR: SANDY NGUYEN
PHOTO: TAGGART-WINTERHALTER

80's inspired bigger hair is making a come back.
Jenny Heroux

BEFORE

JENNY HEROUX
MAKE-UP: JULIE STODDARD
PHOTO: TAGGART-WINTERHALTER

BEFORE

LONG

ARTISTIC HAIR
HAIR: JILL KESTER
MAKE-UP: JAIME QUEENIN
PHOTO: TAGGART-WINTERHALTER

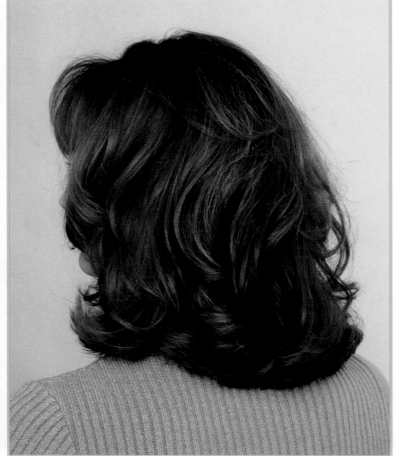

I'm introducing
more **blonde highlights**
into **red bases**.

Barbara Nolasco - Artistic Studio

ARTISTIC HAIR
HAIR: BARBARA NOLASCO
MAKE-UP: JULIE STODDARD
PHOTO: TAGGART-WINTERHALTER

BEFORE

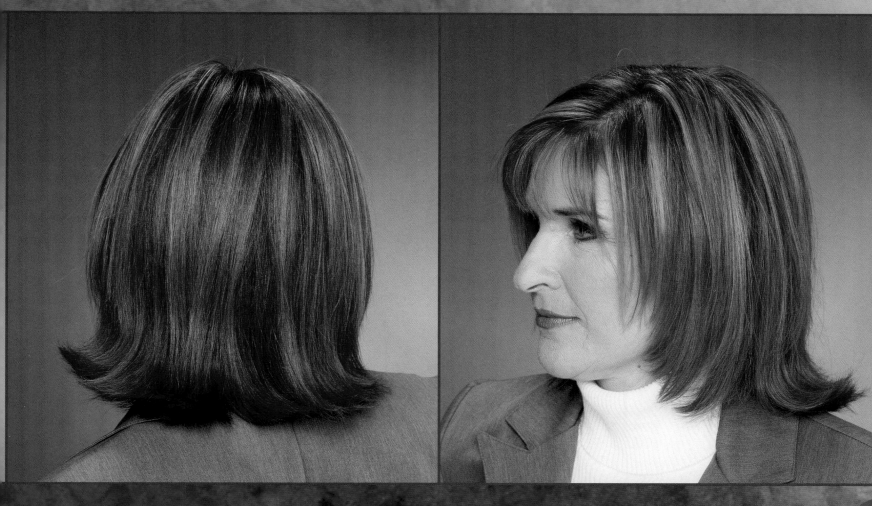

FANTASTIC SAMS
HAIR: BARBARA ANN SILVAS
MAKE-UP: JULIE STODDARD
PHOTO: TAGGART-WINTERHALTER

BEFORE

70

LONG

ROBERT OF PHILADELPHIA
HAIR: JULIE GOGGIN
MAKE-UP: MICHELLE LOUISELLE
PHOTO: ERIC VON LOCKHART

Robert of Philadelphia
HAIR: Lisa Reynolds / Stephanie Ziems
MAKE-UP: Andrey
PHOTO: Eric Von Lockhart

BEFORE

ROBERT OF PHILADELPHIA
HAIR: DIANA MANN & COLLEEN GREENLING
MAKE-UP: MICHELLE LOUISELLE
PHOTO: ERIC VON LOCKHART

ROBERT OF PHILADELPHIA
HAIR: JULIE GOGGIN
MAKE-UP: MICHELLE LOUISELLE
PHOTO: ERIC VON LOCKHART

BEFORE

EFORE

LONG

CELEBRITY

SALLY FIELD

Hair color works to enhance
today's textured cuts.
Carter T. Lund & Associates - Carter T. Lund

PHOTO BY ED GELLER

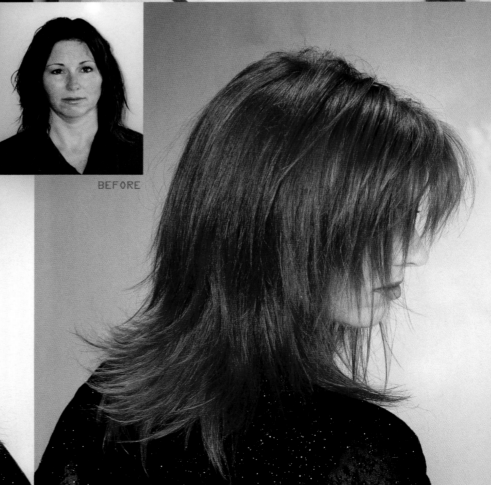

BEFORE

Makeovers

BEFORE

CARTER T. LUND & ASSOCIATES
HAIR: CARTER T. LUND
MAKE-UP: JAIME QUEENIN
PHOTO: TAGGART-WINTERHALTER

MEG RYAN

Teri just needed to glam up a bit.
Fresh color and a texturized style do the trick.

Victor Paul

VICTOR PAUL
MAKE-UP: JULIE STODDARD
PHOTO: TAGGART-WINTERHALTER

PHOTO BY JEFF SLOCOMB

FAITH HILL

JENNY HEROUX
MAKE-UP: JAIME QUEENIN
PHOTO: TAGGART-WINTERHALTER

Nicole has a very young and edgy
look, much like Faith Hill.

A very shattered style
with a bit of kick outwards.

Artistic Hair Team

Longer looks softly frame the face.
Jenny Heroux

PHOTO BY BILL DAVILA

ARTISTIC HAIR
HAIR: ARTISTIC HAIR TEAM
MAKE-UP: JAIME QUEENIN
PHOTO: TAGGART-WINTERHALTER

BEFORE

CELEBRITY Makeovers

77

KATIE COURIC

BEFORE

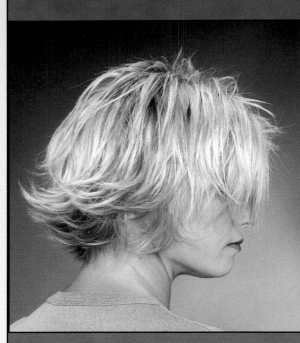

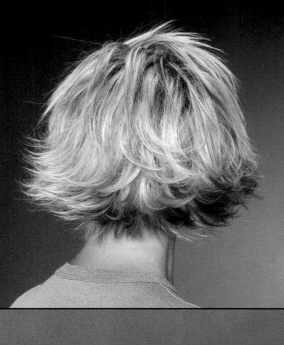

FANTASTIC SAMS
HAIR: CARMEN C. STEVENS
PHOTO: TAGGART-WINTERHALTER

78

Cute, kicky styles
are seen with pieced texture.

Victor Paul

ANNE HECHE

KIM DELANEY

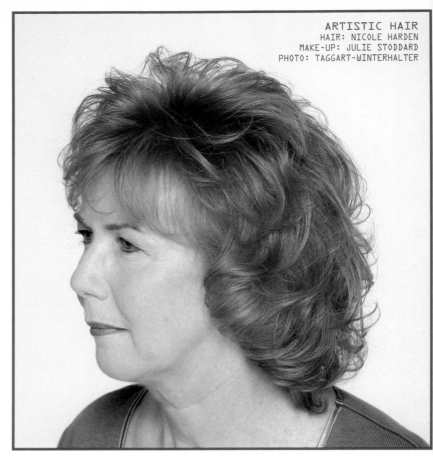

BEFORE

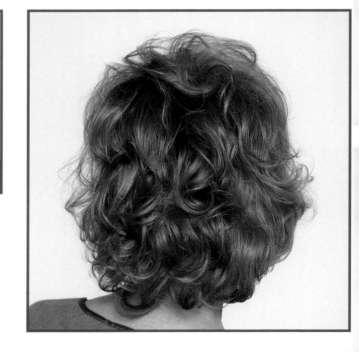

Celebrities like Kim Delaney
are bringing back curls.
Artistic Hair - Nicole Harden

A piecy side swept bang
will be very popular this season.

AGOSTINOS TEMECULA
HAIR: MICHAEL BUTCHER
MAKE-UP: JAIME QUEENIN
PHOTO: TAGGART-WINTERHALTER

BEFORE

SHARON STONE

81

DIANE SAWYER

Shorter styles like Diane Sawyer have a fuller top section with wisps of hair sweeping forward.
Artistic Hair - Jill Kester

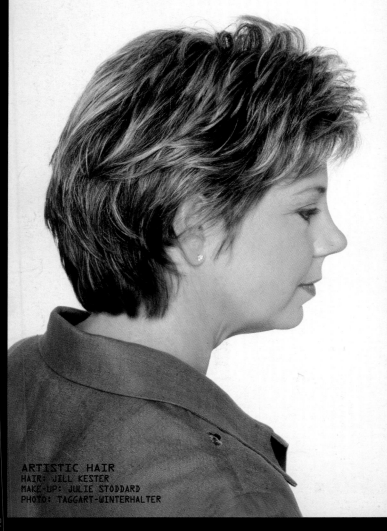

ARTISTIC HAIR
HAIR: JILL KESTER
MAKE-UP: JULIE STODDARD
PHOTO: TAGGART-WINTERHALTER

VIBE STUDIO
HAIR: LAURA CROFT & DEBBIE WATSON
MAKE-UP: JULIE STODDARD
PHOTO: TAGGART-WINTERHALTER

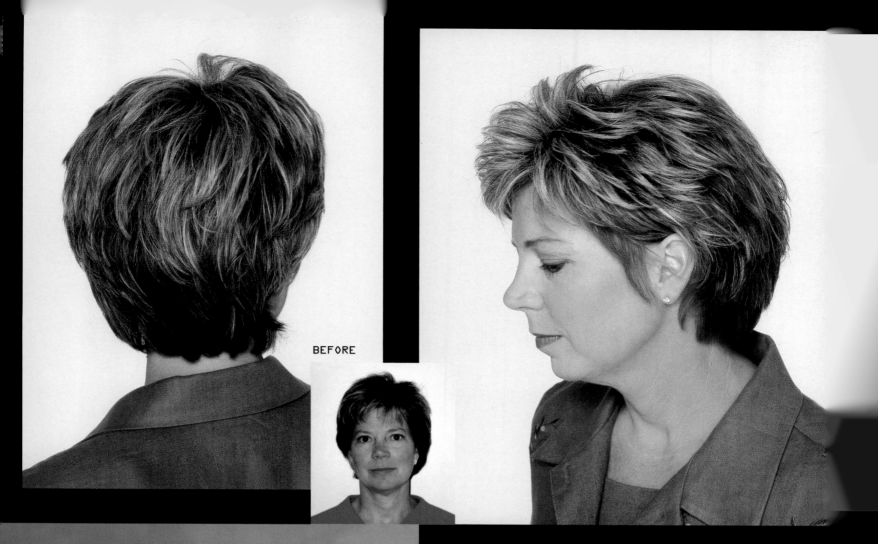

BEFORE

A classic bob can be worn in a variety
of lengths. Like Sela Ward's new style,
bobs have a very sophisticated look.

Vibe Studio - Debbie Watson/ Laura Croft

SELA WARD

BEFORE

Special Collections

ROBERT OF PHILADELPHIA
HAIR: ROBERT DILELLA
COLOR: DAVID TOMLIN
MAKE-UP: ANDREY
PHOTO: ERIC VON LOCKHART

ROBERT OF PHILADELPHIA
HAIR: ROBERT DILELLA & TRACEY DILE
MAKE-UP: ANDREY
PHOTO: ERIC VON LOCKHART

ROBERT OF PHILADELPHIA
HAIR: ROBERT DILELLA & TRACEY DILELLA
MAKE-UP: ANDREY
PHOTO: ERIC VON LOCKHART

BEFO

BEFORE

6

ROBERT OF PHILADELPHIA
HAIR: LOUIS SALVATI, JAY HATT, ROBERT DILELLA & TRACEY DILELLA
MAKE-UP: ANDREY
PHOTO: ERIC VON LOCKHART

ROBERT OF PHILADELPHIA
HAIR: ROBERT DILELLA & TRACEY DILELLA
MAKE-UP: ANDREY
PHOTO: ERIC VON LOCKHART

Convertible

Strong side parting, hair longer and pointed deep from the parting. Strong concave from the crown. Wear heavy bangs or off the face edgy.

Robert DiLella - Robert of Philadelphia

Carefree Unkempt Look

Sweeping to the side. Short to long
from crown to fringe. Very shattered.
Blast dry.

ROBERT OF PHILADELPHIA
HAIR: ROBERT DILELLA & DAVID TOMLIN
MAKE-UP: ANDREY
PHOTO: ERIC VON LOCKHART

This work originates from what we are currently producing in our schools. We used the latest techniques, undercoat shades and disconnected pieces to give these looks a versatile feel and look that depicts the youthfulness of women today.

Martyn Duff - Regional Creative Director, North American Salon Vidal Sassoon

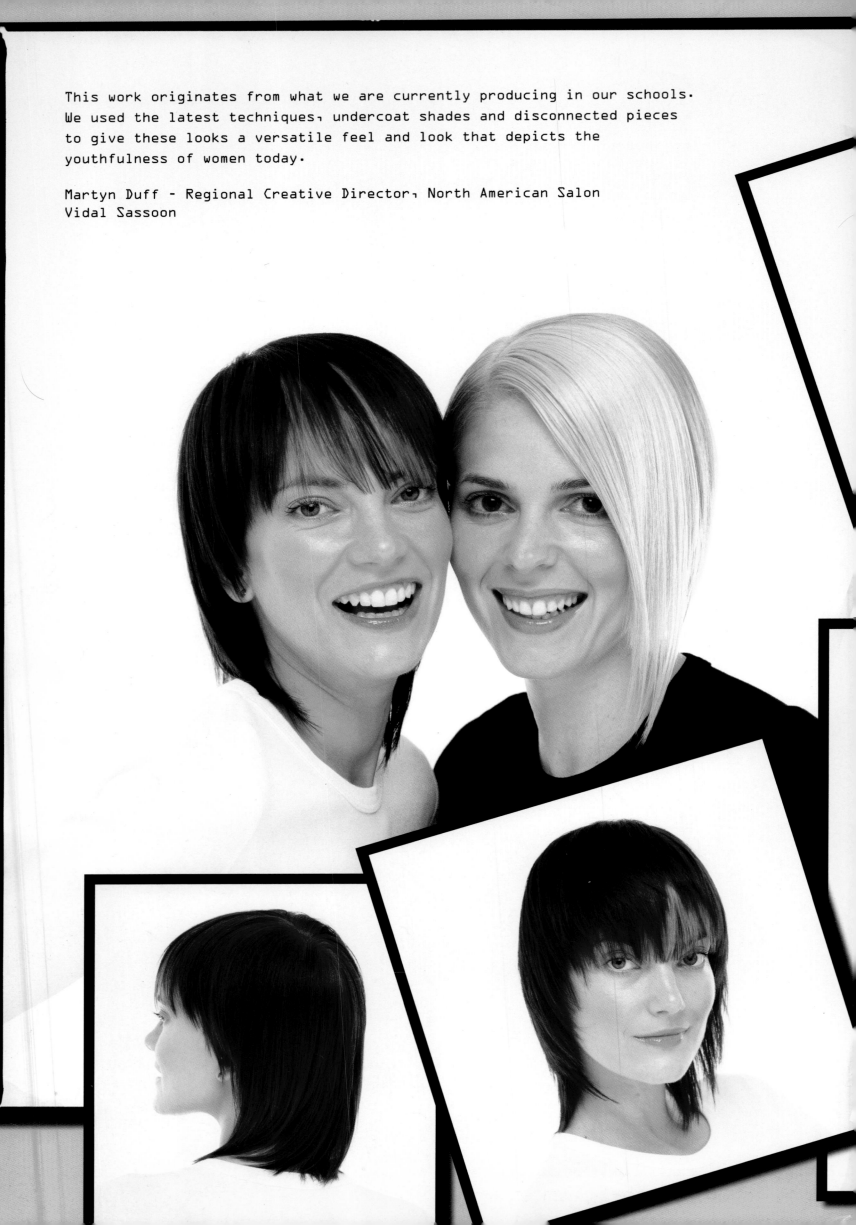

VIDAL SASSOON
USING WELLA COLOR
HAIR: MARTYN DUFF
MAKE-UP: VERED
PHOTO: ERIC VON LOCKHART

SPECIAL Collections

I felt a **modern updated style**
would give Lauren
a young fresh look.

Linda Francipane
Jacques Dessange

JACQUES DESSANGE
HAIR: LINDA FRANCIPANE
MAKE-UP: DANIEL GREEN
PHOTO: ERIC VON LOCKHART

JACQUES DESSANGE
HAIR: CHRISTOPHE BELKACEMI
MAKE-UP: DANIEL GREEN
PHOTO: ERIC VON LOCKHART

Longer layers and straightening Claire's hair gives her a more sophisticated look.
Christophe Belkacemi - Jacques Dessange

SPECIAL Collections

93

TONI & GUY
HAIR: JAMES HERNANDEZ & ALYSON MILLER
MAKE-UP: DANIEL GREEN
PHOTO: ERIC VON LOCKHART

This work is from our **Progression From Zero Zero Collection.**

It's all about **individual choice** - inspired from the **70's and 80's.**

Shorter layers, looser texture and **color** that emphasizes the shape and texture of the cut.

Thomas Osborn
Educational
Director/Creative
Director
Toni & Guy

TONI & GUY
HAIR: THOMAS OSBOURNE & ALYSON MILLER
MAKE-UP: DANIEL GREEN
PHOTO: ERIC VON LOCKHART

Marina is petite with thick, curly hair. A short style with medium layers and a sharp deep angle around her face shows off her beautiful chin and neck. The medium layers take away the heaviness without making the hair look puffy. She can wear this style slicked back with gel, natural and curly or blow dried straight.

SALON AKS
HAIR: ALEX HUANG
MAKE-UP: DANIEL GREEN
PHOTO: ERIC VON LOCKHART

Kathleen has beautiful, naturally wavy hair with blonde highlights. I decided a cut with lots of movement and texture would suit her face shape and lifestyle. The layers emphasize the highlights and shows contrast and movement, while the angle and length open up the face.

Get Your Work Published!

What's Missing? Your Work!

Receive International Recognition when you publish your work in Inspire

Put your name in the limelight and receive the recognition your hard work deserves. Inspire is the only place to be for worldwide recognition.

We are always looking for the latest fresh new looks and styles that are fashionable as well as commercial and are appropriate for salon clientele.

We are looking for handsome men and gorgeous women of all ages to portray the latest new looks and trends. No fantasy work please!

It's So Easy!

Professional photography and good looking models are key to having your work published. Please send only very clean, well protected color slides and transparencies or black and white glossies. Remember to label all your slides with proper credits and submit them with an Inspire model release form.

Request a Submission Package

All the forms and information you need to submit high quality work in one package. AND, if your work is chosen to be in Inspire you'll receive a complimentary book and press release package as our way of saying thanks. Your hard work deserves recognition from your community as well as internationally. Send the press release to the local newspapers, radio stations…Even TV! The response will surprise you.

Call **(800) 634-8500**   Email: **inspire@connix.com**
or visit our website at **www.inspirequarterly.com** to download the forms.

SUBMISSION DEADLINES
- **March 15** - **June 15** - **September 15** - **December 15**

Looking for a GREAT hair photographer? Try one of ours.

Purely Visual Productions
5739 E. Stillwater Ave. #3
Orange Hills CA 92869-3161
(714) 532-4772
ibvisual@aol.com

Eric Von Lockhart Photography
48 West 21st Street
New York NY 10010
(212) 463-0450
evlone@earthlink.net

Tom Carson Photography
611 Ashworth Rd.
Charlotte NC 28211
(704) 364-6457

Que manque-t-il à cette photo?
Votre Travail!
Faites publier vos photos!

Tout le monde souhaite voir ses talents et ses qualités reconnus. Quelle place pourrait être meilleure qu' INSPIRE pour vous faire connaitre?

Nous sommes intéressés de recevoir des photos de coiffures mode destinées aux clientes des salons de coiffure. Nous sommes avides de beaux modèles, de tous âges, hommes ou femmes, mais pas de travaux de haute fantaisie.

De façon à vous faire connaître, indiquez sur chaque photo: le nom du salon, le nom du coiffeur, du maquilleur, et du photographe.

S'il vous plaît n'envoyez que des dias ou négatifs couleurs de bonne qualité ou des photos noir et blanc. Joignez à chaque photo les informations précisées ci-dessus.

Vous êtes intéressé! Bravo!

Pour plus d'information sur la facon de nous transmettre vos photos, téléphonez ou écrivez à notre distributeur officiel.

Que es lo que falta en este retrato?
Tu Trabajo!
Consiga Su Trabajo Publicado!

Todo mundo tiene el deseo de que su talento y habilidades sean reconocidas.

Que mejor lugar que Inspire para recibir este reconocimiento estamos muy interesados en recibir fotografias de modas y aspectos apropiados, para la clientela de salon de belleza.

Nosotros estamos buscando modelos tanto de hombre como de mujer en cualquier edad. No queremos fotos con peinados de fantasta.

Para recibir lo anterior y darle su credito, favor de enviar fotografias muy claras, una por modelo. Favor de enviar fotografias y/o transparencias, muy bien protegidas enviando carta, dando su permiso para la publicacion de la foto.

Esta ud interesado! Grandioso!

Para major informacion de como enviar fotos. Formas de permiso de publicacion para posibles se iones de fotos tomadas en su area. Llamenos o escribanos para recibur guia completa.